THE EAGLES TRIVIA BOOK

Uncover The Epic History & Facts Every Fan

Should Know!

Dale Raynes

ISBN: 978-1-955149-37-2

Questions? Email us at:

support@bridgepress.org

TABLE OF CONTENTS

INTRODUCTION

The Eagles are the most successful rock band in American history. Period. They are also the fourth best-selling music artist in the history of the country.

The Eagles embodied the 1970s like no other band and came to define and illustrate the allure of California. However, they have transcended both time and place. Their classic songs like "Take It Easy" and "Hotel California" are known worldwide and have inspired millions to dream of achieving a "Peaceful Easy Feeling" in the Golden State.

The band emerged from the late-sixties country-rock scene and wrote the genre's most successful and memorable songs. However, they attained their most tremendous success when they dared to transcend the country-rock mold and create a California rock style that is all their own.

It is hard to pinpoint the secret of the seemingly eternal appeal of the band. It is subtle yet unmistakable. But they combined the visceral and reassuring with a challenging and intellectual side. The result was a distinctive and irresistible sound.

Critics have maligned them for years. But we bet they all crank up "Take it Easy" when it comes on the radio. How can anyone resist those opening chords?

We have put together a compendium of questions covering the staggeringly successful and impressive career of the Eagles. So, let's find out once and for all how big a fan you are!

CHAPTER 1:

EARLY YEARS
AND CHILDHOOD

1. In which state did Randy Meisner grow up?

    a. Wisconsin

    b. Oklahoma

    c. Nebraska

    d. Montana

2. True or False. Don came from a very musical family, and his father taught him the guitar.

3. Glenn Frey started playing the piano very early in life. At what age did he start playing?

    a. Four

    b. Five

    c. Six

    d. Seven

4. Glenn gave up the piano. What distracted him from it?

a. The guitar

b. Girls

c. Boy Scouts

d. Boxing

5. Though known as a California band, most of the Eagles were born elsewhere. Which of these members was born in the Golden State?

   a. Joe Walsh

   b. Timothy B. Schmitt

   c. Bernie Leadon

   d. Don Henley

6. Joe Walsh was inspired by childhood tragedy to set up a charity. What is the cause Joe diligently supports?

   a. Fighting cancer

   b. Supporting military veterans

   c. Fighting forest fires

   d. Alzheimer awareness

7. Don Henley is fairly nostalgic about his childhood. Which of these landmarks from his early years did he buy as an adult?

a. His mother's house

b. His grandmother's house

c. His father's store

d. Major storefronts in his hometown

8. Who was Timothy B. Schmitt's childhood musical inspiration?

   a. The Beatles

   b. Johnny Cash

   c. The Kingston Trio

   d. Waylon Jennings

9. Glenn wanted to go to Michigan State. However, he wasn't accepted. Why not?

   a. He has a criminal record

   b. His grades were low

   c. He didn't show up for the interview

   d. The principal wouldn't sign his application

10. Why did Glenn leave Michigan for California?

   a. To avoid trouble with the law

   b. To avoid the draft

   c. To forget a bad relationship

   d. For the music scene

11. Don is known as a fairly intellectual lyricist. What were his majors in college?

    a. English and history

    b. Comparative literature and philosophy

    c. Philosophy and English

    d. History and economics

12. True or False. Randy's early band, the Dynamics, once opened for Jimi Hendrix.

13. A country superstar produced Shiloh's first album. Who was the producer?

    a. Kenny Rogers

    b. Willie Nelson

    c. Dolly Parton

    d. Merle Haggard

14. Don Henley and Glenn Frey first met in Los Angeles. In which famous music haunt did that fateful meeting take place?

    a. Whisky a Go Go

    b. The Troubadour

    c. The Rainbow Room

    d. Roxy

15. How did Randy Meisner meet Glenn Frey?

    a. They played at the same venue

    b. They dated the same girl

    c. They met at a bar

    d. They met hitchhiking

16. Glenn, Don, Randy Meisner, and Bernie Leadon played one show with Linda Ronstadt. Where did it take place?

    a. Six Flags

    b. Disneyland

    c. Sea World

    d. The Bronx Zoo

17. Bernie Leadon once replaced a member of Crosby, Stills, Nash, and Young in a band. Which member did he replace?

    a. David Crosby

    b. Stephen Stills

    c. Graham Nash

    d. Neil Young

18. Which hand did Glenn Frey use to play guitar?

    a. Left

b. Right

c. Left, but he was actually right-handed

d. Right, but he was actually left-handed

19. Linda Ronstadt would later cover an Eagles song to great acclaim. Which song did she record?

    a. "Hotel California"

    b. "Take it Easy"

    c. "The Best of My Love"

    d. "Desperado"

20. When the James Gang first toured the United Kingdom, which notorious British rock star took Joe under his wing and taught him how to party?

    a. Elton John

    b. Keith Moon

    c. Eric Clapton

    d. Jimmy Page

ANSWERS

1. C- Nebraska. Scottsbluff, Nebraska, to be more precise. However, he took every opportunity to play in that rural atmosphere. Randy explains, "I heard Elvis Presley and Conway Twitty, which made me want to get an acoustic guitar. So at around 12 or 13, I got an acoustic guitar and took some lessons. I played some PTA meetings out in the country."

2. False. "I used to sit on my front porch down there on this dirt road in Gainesville on this metal collider just sliding back and forth and back and forth, trying to figure out how that guitar worked. Where do you put your fingers? How do you make chords? And there wasn't a music school. There was no money to be had in my family for lessons if there was a music school. So, I was pretty much self-taught, and it turned out that I gave myself kind of basic ear training by listening to new stuff on the radio or listening to my stuff on my dad's tape recorder and just playing it over and over and over until I could figure it out on guitar."

3. B- Five. Glenn remembered, "My mother started me on piano when I was five years old. They bought an old, used upright for about ten bucks and put it in the basement of the house [where] we lived in Royal Oak. I grew up at 1616 Wyandotte, two blocks from Benjamin Franklin. The house doesn't exist anymore — it was knocked down. At my mother's insistence, I started taking piano lessons and continued to take lessons 'til I was 12." Sounds like we can thank Glenn's mother for the Eagles.

4. C- Boy Scouts. Frey remembers that at age 12, "I enjoyed piano for the first four or five years, but then started to sour on it. As things like the Boy Scouts and other opportunities started to present themselves, I grew a little tired of it by the time I got to be 12. So, I basically stopped playing and didn't play for three or four years."

5. D- Timothy B. Schmitt. Tim was born in Oakland. None of the original lineup was born in the state. However, Bernie grew up in San Diego, California, and cut his teeth on the bluegrass scene in the city. It is an interesting irony how little connection they had

to California, considering they are considered the epitome of South California rock.

6. B- Supporting military veterans. Joe's father died while on duty in Okinawa, Japan, when Joe was a child. The guitarist says, "War is hell for everyone involved. I lost my father when I was a baby before I could even make a memory of him. I stopped counting the number of friends I lost in the Vietnam War or who came home forever scarred mentally or physically or both. We've only just begun to appreciate the long-term impacts on our troops home from Iraq. And in Afghanistan, the longest war in American history continues to drag on with no end in sight. I had to do something, and seeing as though rock-and-roll seems to be what I do best, it's also the least I could do for those who have served and continue to serve our country." Therefore, he started VetsAid, and all the proceeds go to veterans in need.

7. Trick question. All four. Don had to leave his home in California after the Northridge earthquake. He moved back to Texas, where he grew up, taking a

great interest in Cass County. He explained that he once did not allow the area to put up signs associating the area with him but now has learned to embrace it. "They're putting up billboards on the interstate: 'Home of ... ' I've not allowed them to do that for 30 years, and I finally relented. I said, 'Okay, put it up there, but when it starts deteriorating ... ' I was halfway through before I called it Cass County, and why not? That's where a lot of the musical influences came from. And my hometown needs a shot in the arm."

8. C- The Kingston Trio. Timothy remembered, "I had a band, my friends and I who eventually made records together, we started copying a lot of those songs, especially The Kingston Trio. That's when we first started going on stage as strummers and singers. It was early high school, maybe [early] as 13 or 14 years old."

9. D- The principal wouldn't sign his application. Glenn recalled, "I'd wanted to go to Michigan State but couldn't get the principal to sign my application — we'd had some problems. I ended up going to

junior college and did three things: went to the parking lot and got high, went to the lunchroom and looked at girls, and went to folk club meetings. I basically wasted my parents' money."

10. B- To avoid the draft. But if you said A and D, you are not wrong either. Glenn explained, "I didn't really see much of a future for myself in the Detroit music scene. I had some other problems and things going on — it was probably better to go to California before I got in trouble with the police. Let's just say I was creating some problems for myself. To tell you the truth ... the Vietnam War and the draft were really important issues at that time. If you went to college and got a student deferment, as soon as you got out, you were a 1a status again. That wasn't every attractive."

11. C- Philosophy, and English. He got his degree at North Texas State University. Don describes himself as an "enlightened redneck."

12. True. Kind of. The band was trying to break it big in New York and failing miserably. Randy remembers, "We got there, and we stayed in one bedroom at The Earl Hotel in the middle of summer. It was like a

hundred degrees. We all had cots, and there were cockroaches all over, and we couldn't breathe." They finally got a big break playing with Hendrix. Or so they thought. Randy remembered, "We finally opened the club. Jimi Hendrix was the opener. Charlie and Brian got us some nice clothes, some bell-bottoms, and we get ready to go on, and Jimi Hendrix comes in. We were excited to meet him. So, he goes up, does the fire thing, burns the guitar, and destroys the whole P.A. system. The guy comes back and says, you lucked out; you don't even have to play."

13. Kenny Rogers.

14. The Troubadour. That important L.A. haunt played a significant role in the development of the band. Don says Glenn "walked up to me one night in the Troubadour and handed me a beer, and he just started talking to me. You know, the Troubadour Bar was the center of the universe at that point in time." Randy remembers, "We drank a lot of beer there. Randy Newman, Steve Martin, Jim Morrison, all these people we'd know hung out here. We'd go down there and have a few beers. That's how I

started the song 'Take It To The Limit.' I went back to my house one night from the Troubadour. It was real late at night. I was by myself and started singing and playing the line 'all alone at the end of the evening.' That's where it started."

15. They met hitchhiking. Meisner remembers, "The first time I met Glenn Frey, he was hitchhiking. So I gave him a ride in my little Austin Healy Sprite. I didn't know him. We didn't know we were even gonna be in a group together."

16. B- Disneyland.

17. B- Stephen Stills. Don Felder was in that band, too. They were based out of Gainesville, Florida. Felder remembered, "Stephen Stills and I had a band together in Gainesville. I think we were 14 and 15 years old. My mom would drive us around to these little events because we didn't have a car or a driver's license or anything. Bernie showed up and picked me up actually at a bus station where I was coming back from a little town called Lake City, about 30 minutes away, where I've gone up by myself and played this little women's tea party in the afternoon. So, he had a

car; he was 16. He picked me up at the bus station and actually wound up replacing Stevens Stills in that band."

18. Right, but he was actually left-handed. Or something like that. Don says, "He was something of a freak of nature: He played guitar right-handed, but played golf left-handed, at least when he was driving the ball. But he putted right-handed. When we played baseball or softball, he would bat and throw left-handed."

19. "Desperado." Don was highly flattered. He said, "I was extremely flattered that Linda recorded 'Desperado.' It was really her who popularized the song. Her version was very poignant and beautiful."

20. B- Keith Moon. Joe says, "The James Gang were opening up for The Who when they premiered 'Tommy' in Europe, and Keith Moon decided that he liked me and that we should stay up for the entire tour. He taught me the basics of hotel damage, blowing stuff up, and anarchic chaos in general. He was my mentor. And of course, I embellished it later with things like chainsaws. 'You took a chainsaw on

the road?' Yeah. But I found that you didn't have to really use it that much. Walking up to the front desk with one usually got a lot accomplished."

DID YOU KNOW

- The harmony vocals are an integral part of the Eagles' sound. The easy-breezing sound is often associated with California. However, the harmonies originated from the Michigan garage band scene. Glenn remembers, "The best band in Birmingham was called the Four of Us. The leader of the band was Gary Burrows. A guy named Jeff Alborell who played bass, rhythm guitar was a guy named Ziggy, and there were two drummers, a kid named Jimmy Fox and a guy named Pete. They were the only band I saw going around clubs in Detroit that really had all the vocals. Every band in Detroit was either patterned after Mitch Ryder and the Detroit Wheels — the greaser soul-band vein — or they wanted to be the Stones, the Animals, a Pretty Things sort of thing, with just one singer and not a lot of background vocals. And I must say before I met Gary Burrows, I didn't think too much about harmonies and that kind of thing. But that's what he was into, and we spent a lot of time working on vocals."

- Randy Meisner was the bassist for Poco, one of the trailblazers of the country-rock movement. However, his brief membership in the band was troubled. Meisner remembers, "We were like the first country-rock group. I was real into R&B, so I considered myself a good R&B bass player. George Grantham, Poco's drummer, could play anything and Rusty Young with the steel guitar and Jimmy Messina. Rusty and Jimmy had written some songs. I don't think I really wrote anything for the band. I left after about a year." The band tried to write him out of their history. Randy says, "They took me out of the painting. They left my voice on and my bass parts, and on one song, they took my voice off. But all my background harmonies and bass parts are on there." But Randy is still very proud of his time with the band, and rightfully so. He explains, "With Poco and the Eagles, there's a common musical thread that runs throughout with the disciples being The Byrds, Buffalo Springfield, and The Flying Burrito Brothers." But unlike those bands, Leadon wanted to be in a genuinely successful band this time. As he explained, "When this band started, we said, we want it all. Critical acclaim, artistic success, and financial success. It wasn't like we want to make a pretty good album, so our girlfriends like us. No, it was 'we want to be the best fucking band there is.'"

- Meisner was comfortable out of the limelight. Perhaps too comfortable. The other band members wanted him to take a more central role out of appreciation for his talent. But that was not his style. Randy recalls, "I was always kind of shy ... They wanted me to stand in the middle of the stage to sing, but I liked to be out of the spotlight." A massive rift emerged after refused Meisner to sing in one show in Knoxville, Tennessee. Randy was indignant because he had the flu. He remembers, "We've been out for a total of 11 months, and everybody was starting to feel the strain. My ulcer was starting to act up, and I had a bad case of the flu, as well. Still, we all sounded great onstage, the audience loved the show, and we were being called back for another encore. 'No way,' I said. I was too sick and generally fed up. I decided I wasn't going back out. That was the end ... I really felt like I was a member of the group, not a part of it."

In another interview, he said, "Those last days on the road were the worst. Nobody was talking to me or would hang out after shows or do anything. I was made an outcast of the band I'd helped start." Although Randy would only leave during the "Hotel California" tour, the rift emerged after "One of these Nights." When he left, he cited exhaustion and summarized the issue by saying, "All that stuff and all the arguing amongst the Eagles is over now. Well, at least for me."

CHAPTER 2:

THE DEBUT ALBUM

1. The Flying Burrito Brothers have inspired the Eagles and included Bernie Leadon as a member. How many other members did that classic band have over the years?

   a. Over 30
   b. Over 40
   c. Over 50
   d. Over 60

2. Which country legend gave Don Henley a place to crash in L.A.?

   a. Waylon Jennings
   b. Kenny Rogers
   c. Willie Nelson
   d. Merle Haggard

3. In 1971, the band was signed by David Geffen to his label Asylum Records. Who introduced them to Geffen?

a. Neil Young

b. Linda Ronstadt

c. Carly Simon

d. Jackson Browne

4. Where did the young, new band go to have their first rehearsals and work out their sound?

a. Aspen, Colorado

b. Annapolis, Maryland

c. Crater Lake, Oregon

d. Newport, Rhode Island

5. Though they rehearsed out of the city, Don says the band really coalesced in Los Angeles. In which part of the city did their intense rehearsals create the trademark Eagles sound?

a. Hollywood

b. Santa Monica

c. The San Fernando Valley

d. Pasadena

6. Where was the first Eagles album recorded?

a. Los Angeles

b. Nashville

   c. London

   d. Miami

7. Which successful producer worked on the debut album?

   a. Martin Birch

   b. Jerry Wexler

   c. Glyn Johns

   d. Phil Spector

8. Who wrote the famous line, "I'm standing on a corner in Winslow, Arizona," in "Take It Easy?"

   a. Don Henley

   b. Jackson Browne

   c. Glenn Frey

   d. J.D. Souther

9. Where did the band shoot the album cover for the first album?

   a. The Grand Canyon

   b. Joshua Tree

   c. Big Sur

   d. Yellowstone

10. The song "Witchy Woman" was inspired by the

famous wife of which writer?

    a. Ernest Hemingway

    b. F. Scott Fitzgerald

    c. Philip Roth

    d. J.D. Salinger

11. True or False. The birds you can hear on "Earlybird" belonged to Glenn Frey.

12. True or False. "Witchy Woman" was also a protest against what Don saw as the unhealthy practice of witchcraft by many in the hippie movement at the time?

13. After completing their first album, the band was opened for which somewhat mismatched headlining act?

    a. Yes

    b. King Crimson

    c. Emerson, Lake & Palmer

    d. The Moody Blues

14. What was the first Eagles' No.1 hit on the Billboard charts?

    a. "Take it Easy"

b. "Witchy Woman"

c. "Tequila Sunrise"

d. "Best of My Love"

15. True or False. Don wanted the band to have a showier image like Kiss or Elton John but was overruled by Glenn.

16. Which well-known musician took Glenn Frey under his wing early in Frey's career?

    a. Neil Young

    b. Bob Seger

    c. Dr. John

    d. Gram Parsons

17. At first, Glenn and Don had trouble writing and working together. So which song started their productive writing partnership?

    a. "Tequila Sunrise"

    b. "On the Border"

    c. "Desperado"

    d. "Witchy Woman"

18. How much did it cost to produce the band's debut album?

a. $25,000

b. $125,000

c. $225,000

d. $325,000

19. Which song was added to the album at the record company's insistence, despite the producer's objections?

    a. "Earlybird"

    b. "Train Leaves Here This Morning"

    c. "Tryin"

    d. "Most of Us Are Sad"

20. Jack Tempchin wrote the song "Peaceful Easy Feeling." What other Eagles classic did he write?

    a. "One of these Nights"

    b. "Witchy Woman"

    c. "Already Gone"

    d. "Life in the Fast Lane"

ANSWERS

1. D- Over 60. If you include all reincarnations of the band, the number is staggering.

2. B- Kenny Rogers. Kenny was a mentor to Don and played a significant part in the formation of the Eagles. Kenny took Don's first band, Shiloh, as a project and helped promote them. When Rogers passed away, Don released a statement: "In addition to his tremendous talent, Kenny was a generous and caring man, a wise mentor to so many of us. He loved his friends, his family, his fellow musicians, and his fans, and they loved him right back. Fifty years ago, The Gambler took a gamble on me, and my first band from small-town Texas and his big-hearted support launched many careers, including mine. He also gave me some of the best career advice I ever got. 'You'd better be nice to the people you meet on the way up because you're going to meet those same people on the way back down.'"

3. D- Jackson Browne. Browne co-wrote the Eagles' first big hit and introduced them to the man who got

them signed. Browne's contribution to the band is immense.

4. A- Aspen, Colorado. When the band played in clubs there, very few people showed up. But it turns out that was a good thing. Randy explained, "We played this club. Every night I would record us on a little stereo cassette. I got this mixing board from Radio Shack, took all the mics, and recorded everything. It sounded really good because nobody was in the club. All the kids from the colleges were taking their exams, so we'd get like three people a night. We were just playing to a dry stage, so it recorded really well."

5. C- The San Fernando Valley. Don remembers, "Rehearsing in a little wooden shack called Bud's (after its owner), just off Ventura Boulevard, near Barham Boulevard. Bud's place was tucked into a parking lot behind a liquor store called the Spirit Locker, which has been renamed now. I also remember rehearsing, later on, in a building that was located near the intersection of Ventura Boulevard and Vineland Avenue. This is the place where Glyn Johns came and heard us for the second time and

finally decided that he would produce us. So, you could say that the Eagles band really coalesced, really began, in the San Fernando Valley."

6. C- London. At Olympic Studios.

7. C- Glyn Johns. The band wanted a tough sound and hired the producer known for his work with the Rolling Stones and The Who. Glenn explained, "We just didn't wanna make another limp-wristed L.A. country-rock record. They were all too smooth and glassy. We wanted a tougher sound." However, they did not regret their choice. Don says, "Doing our first album with Glyn Johns was a stroke of genius on everyone's part because he was a real strong producer in the face of first-album weirdness."

8. B- Jackson Browne. However, Browne got stuck after that line and couldn't think of a follow-up. Therefore, Glenn wrote the rest of the verse before Browne completed the song.

9. B- Joshua Tree. Don says, "The Joshua Tree National Monument, in 1971, was more wild and untouched than it is today. It was a magical place. There was a

pervasive feeling that we were embarking on a momentous journey; there was an air of portent in the positive sense."

10. B- F. Scott Fitzgerald. Don Henley said he wrote those lyrics while "reading a book about the life of F. Scott Fitzgerald's troubled wife, Zelda, who, in her thirties and forties, drifted in and out of psychiatric hospitals suffering from schizophrenia (or more likely, bipolar disorder), while her husband's health and career spiraled downward, due to his abuse of alcohol."

11. False. They were actually stock sound effects. Don says, "They were taken from a sound-effects library. I thought — and still think — it was corny, but it wasn't my song. Adding the chirping sounds was the decision of both the song's author and our producer. Forty-four years later, it really doesn't matter, does it?"

12. False. Don was kind of charmed by it. The lyric writer recalls, "all things occult were popular in those days—Ouija boards, séances, palm reading, etc. A lot of the girls were into what was called white

witchcraft; that is, they were practitioners of folk magic for benevolent purposes, as distinguished from malevolent witchcraft or black magic. I think some of them practiced a little of both. I thought it was charming and seductive, but I never took any of it seriously. For the most part, it was just a phase people were passing through, part of the overall youth movement and the quest for spirituality, which included a re-enchantment with the old ways. It was harmless fun."

13. A- Yes.

14. D- "Best of My Love." Though their early singles did well, they did not chart as high as you may expect. "Take it Easy" made No. 12, "Witchy Woman" No. 9, and "Tequila Sunrise" only reached No. 64 but became a fan favorite.

15. False. Don always shied away from the showier side of 1970s rock. As he explained, "We don't go in for glitter or glam rock. We don't wear gorilla suits or aqualungs. Ultimately, the music survives, and that's what we're most interested in. It will establish the image for you without even working at it."

16. B- Bob Seger. They had met when Glenn was 16. Glenn recalled, "We started hanging out together. We'd drive around all night and smoke dope and listen to the radio. We'd drive to Ann Arbor and hang with (musician) Scott Richardson at his house, go to the Fifth Dimension Club and see The Who and Jimi Hendrix there. We were all trying to scratch the puzzle: how to make it in the music business. Bob allowed me to start playing on his records … I was impressed. He was like my big brother for those couple of years before I left for California." When Frey died, Seger said, "I knew him for 50 years. He was a great kid. I always kind of thought of him as my baby brother, a little bit. He was fucking brilliant. He was a joy to be around. I always looked forward to seeing him. It was always memorable. He had an amazing sense of humor and was just smart, whip-smart."

17. C- "Desperado." Don remembers the process of writing the song fondly. "Glenn came over to write one day, and I showed him this unfinished tune that I had been holding for so many years. I said, 'When

I play it and sing it, I think of Ray Charles – Ray Charles and Stephen Foster. It's really a Southern gothic thing, but we can easily make it more Western.' Glenn leaped right on it – filled in the blanks and brought structure. And that was the beginning of our songwriting partnership – that's when we became a team."

18. B- $125,000. That was quite a bit for an unknown band at the time.

19. A- Earlybird. Geffen had the band record the song in L.A. Johns was livid and had it re-recorded in London, even though he did not like the song.

20. C- "Already Gone." Jack says the inspiration for the song came when he was living in a sort of musicians' commune. He recalls, "We'd sit in front of the picture window and watch the beautiful girls on the bus stop bench and fall in love with them until their bus came. We talked in those days about how love never seems to show up until you stop looking for it. But, as young guys, we were unable to stop looking for love even for one day."

DID YOU KNOW

- The name, Eagles, came to the band while they wandered the Mojave Desert in California. However, the guys were whacked out of their minds on peyote and tequila at the time. Therefore, their recollection of the events is not very clear. However, comedian Steve Martin claims that the idea for the name was his. In his autobiography, he says that he suggested The Eagles, and Glenn Frey changed it to Eagles. But Don says that the peyote inspired the idea. He remembers, "In the early going, we went out to Joshua Tree and did that peyote ritual a couple of times. I think that J.D. Souther and Ned Doheny were along on one of the campouts. On one of those trips, Glenn saw a huge eagle fly right over him at a relatively low altitude. Naturally, we took this as a sign." Glenn also remembers those trips, as he explained, "I think everybody got higher than they ever imagined anybody could be. And it was a good thing. We were after getting into life, deeper and better and more, and surrendering." He remembers the band called him to see an eagle above just as he was zipping his pants up from going to the bathroom.

- Don sees "Take It Easy" as part of a long American literary and cultural tradition — the tribute to the open road. The singer explains, "The song's primary appeal, I think, is that it evokes a sense of motion, both musically and lyrically. The romance of the open road. The lure of adventure and possibility – Route 66, the Blue Ridge Parkway, Pacific Coast Highway. Great American writers from Thomas Wolfe to Jack Kerouac to Wallace Stegner have addressed this theme of the restlessness of the American spirit, of our need to keep moving, especially from east to west, in search of freedom, identity, fortune, and this elusive thing we call home."

- Glyn Johns was more than just a producer for the Eagles. In a very real sense, he crafted the band's trademark sound with the four-part harmonies. When the producer was first brought to see the band by David Geffen, Johns was unimpressed with what he heard. He felt that the band had no clear identity and didn't know if it wanted to play rock 'n roll or country. However, when he first heard them sing four-part harmonies, he realized the band was something special. The producer explained, "They were a harmony band. The sound they made vocally was extraordinary. They were a country-rock band."

- The harmonies were indeed one of the things that made the band stand out from the crowd. Randy explained, "Glenn would sing lead, and then we'd find places to sing. After a while, when you played together, it was almost natural what harmony you'd be singing. Like with me, I did a lot of high parts. There was a certain timbre in our voices that when we sang together, it was like an instrument."

CHAPTER 3:

"DESPERADO"

1. The song "Desperado" was written in a house built on a cliff at the top of Laurel Canyon. So, who lived in that house before and gave it 'good vibes'?

   a. James Taylor

   b. Arlo Guthrie

   c. Frank Zappa

   d. Roger McGuinn

2. True or False. The band was determined to have even bigger hits on their second album than the big three from the debut.

3. True or False. When the band recorded "Desperado," they lived with an orchestra and made friends with members of the London Philharmonic.

4. True or False. The band recorded their early albums outside of L.A. because they wanted to be away from the city music scene's well-known distractions and party atmosphere.

5. What was the first album to feature Don Felder on guitar?

   a. "Eagles"
   b. "Desperado"
   c. "On the Border"
   d. "One of These Nights"

6. Don was a guitar teacher before making it big. So, which future star learned how to play from Felder before making it big?

   a. Tom Petty
   b. Chrissie Hynde
   c. Rick Nielsen
   d. Tom Verlaine

7. Speaking of guitar teaching, which legendary guitarist taught Don some of his best licks?

   a. Eric Clapton
   b. Jimi Hendrix
   c. Jeff Beck
   d. Duane Allman

8. "My Man" was a moving tribute to the deceased Gram Parsons. Which member of the band wrote it?

a. Bernie Leadon

b. Randy Meisner

c. Glenn Frey

d. Don Henley

9. Glyn Johns was a difficult taskmaster by all accounts. But he got along with everyone in the band aside from one member. Which member was it?

a. Bernie Leadon

b. Randy Meisner

c. Glenn Frey

d. Don Henley

10. Who produced most of the songs in "On the Border?"

a. Bill Szymczyk

b. Glyn Johns

c. Don Henley

d. Elliott Scheiner

11. "On the Border" was primarily recorded in Eagles' home base, Los Angeles. In which Angelino studio was the album recorded?

a. Capitol Studios

b. Sunset Sound Recorders

c. The Record Plant

d. The Village Studios

12. Some of the copies of "On the Border" included a message carved into the run-out groove. What was the message?

    a. "He who hesitates misses breakfast"

    b. "He who hesitates is lunch"

    c. "He who hesitates is served for dinner"

    d. "He who hesitates misses cocktail hour"

13. The song "Best of My Love" includes a reference to Guido. Who is he?

    a. He worked at one of the bands favorite restaurants

    b. He worked at a gas station the band frequented

    c. He worked at a bar the band liked

    d. He was not a real person

14. True or False. The song "Best of My Love" topped the easy listening charts.

15. True or False. The band was unhappy with the edited version of "Best of My Love" that topped the Billboard charts.

16. The title song, "On the Border," was more political than most Eagles songs. Which political event was the song referring to?

   a. The Watergate Scandal
   b. The Vietnam War
   c. The energy crisis
   d. The Battle of the Sexes tennis match

17. In the liner notes, T.N.T.S. is credited with background vocals on the track. That refers to "help" the band got from a favorite drink. What drink does the T stand for?

   a. Tanqueray
   b. Tondena
   c. Tito's
   d. Tapatio

18. "On the Border" includes a cover version of the song "Ol' 55." Who wrote the original song?

   a. Bob Seger
   b. Joni Mitchell
   c. Tom Waits
   d. Mike Bloomfield

19. The band was invited to play in the famous California Jam show of April 6, 1974. How many people attended the festival?

    a. 100,000

    b. 200,000

    c. 300,000

    d. 400,000

20. Jackson Browne filled in for Felder at the California Jam show. So why did Felder miss the show?

    a. He was drunk

    b. He got caught in traffic

    c. He was recording a solo album

    d. The birth of his son

ANSWERS

1. D- Roger McGuinn. As Don remembers, "it was one of those little houses that hung suspended off a steep hillside and was held up by stilts (vertical posts). When the Santa Ana winds would whip through the canyon, that house would sway, and it could be very unsettling. I was told that it was built to do that (but even then, it remained spooky). The owner also told me of that house that Roger McGuinn, the leader of The Byrds, had formerly lived there, so the place had good vibes, even if it did have hideous orange shag carpet."

2. False. The band saw themselves as more of an album band and wanted to be taken seriously. Henley explains, "Our main goal, at the beginning and throughout our career, was to write good, memorable songs, make albums that had little or no filler, that were consistent from beginning to end in terms of songwriting and production. We also wanted to be a good live act. We wanted to be the whole package. We didn't always meet our goals, but we tried." He

explained, "Having three hit singles on our very first album scared us a little bit. It's not as if we weren't grateful or excited about it. We were amazed, actually. But at the same time, we didn't want to become just another Top 40 hit machine."

3. False. Yes, the London Philharmonic was there. But relations between the band and the symphony were frosty. Don recalls, "Several of them being crotchety old farts who were pissed off because they were required to play some whole notes. Some of the violinists had actually brought chessboards with them, set them up between their chairs, and were playing chess between takes. Let's just say that they were not enamored with the lore of the American West, at least not in the form of pop balladry. They were bored shitless, and I was scared stiff."

4. False. Glyn Johns was intent on getting the band away from home. However, they were never particularly happy about that. Don explains, "We loved London – still do – but being able to sleep in your own bed, being able to eat the foods you love and see people who are dear to you in the locales you are familiar

with brings a comfort that aids in the creative process. Glyn Johns and our managers thought it wise to get us out of L.A. and away from what they considered to be the inherent distractions of the place. But what they failed to understand is that Los Angeles and its environs have always been a big part of our inspiration, our imaginative touchstones — the ocean, the mountains, the desert."

5. C- "On the Border." Glenn remembered, "I've been a Don Felder fan for about a year and a half. Ever since I heard him playing in a dressing room in Boston one night. I saw him at a concert in L.A. and asked if he'd come down and put some slide on "Good Day in Hell," but with every take, he just blew us all away. If he isn't Duane Allman reincarnate, I don't know who the fuck is."

6. Tom Petty. They both lived in Gainesville, Florida, at the time. Don remembers, "Little Tommy Petty. He was playing bass in this band called the Epics, and he thought it was awkward to be fronting a band playing bass and singing. So, he wanted to learn to play guitar so he could write songs instead of

playing bass, so I gave him guitar lessons. I helped with a little bit of the arrangement on a couple of their songs and their shows. I went to just hang out. We were friends. We were in Battles of the Bands together."

7. D- Duane Allman. When he was playing in Gainesville. Don says, "Duane Allman and Gregg Allman were in different bands in that time called, like the Allman Joys or The Spotlights. Duane taught me how to play slide guitar one night on the floor of his mom's house in Daytona Beach [at] about 2:30 in the morning."

8. Bernie Leadon. The two had played together in The Flying Burrito Brothers band. Leadon left because the band was unable to obtain commercial success. Bernie remembers that Gram was "very gregarious, outgoing, funny. We were all so young that we didn't think of ourselves as being possible alcoholics or addicts, but everybody in our peer group drank and did drugs. Certain people had a tendency to go over the edge. We all would have a couple of beers and maybe smoke a joint or something, but Gram tended

to get out beyond that."

9. Glenn Frey. The problem started out as an argument over musical direction and turned into something significantly worse. Johns remembers, "Glenn Frey and I never got on. He thought they were a rock 'n roll band, and they weren't … But Frey, because he came from fucking Detroit, thought they were a rock 'n roll band. But they wouldn't know rock 'n roll if they fell over it." Johns says that drugs also took their toll on the frayed relationship. "Glenn wanted to get high in the studio, and I wouldn't let him. It wasn't anything musical. But that thing about me being strict in the studio is bollocks! Then again, I tried being nice for a while, and it didn't really work. Schoolmasterly? I spent years, very long days, with people stoned out of their tree, and the minute I had control over them, I decided I wouldn't put up with it anymore because I'd wasted so much of my life waiting for people to get their shit together." Glenn, for his part, was a lot more measured and insisted, "I just think it was time for a change … We're still friends."

10. Bill Szymczyk. Aside from two songs produced by

Glyn, Bill produced the album and would remain the band's primary producer for several albums. Don said the main difference between the two was in his drum sound. "There's a lot less echo with Bill, for one thing. There's more of a raw and funky presence. Glyn had a stamp he put on his records which is a deep echo that is really smooth like ice cream."

11. The Record Plant. The sister studio of the famous New York one opened its doors in 1969.

12. "He who hesitates is lunch." It was one of a series of joke sentences they carved on some pressings of their albums. "One of these Nights" had "DONT WORRY — NOTHING WILL BE OKAY!" inscribed on it.

13. He worked at one of the band's favorite restaurants. Guido was the maître d' at Dan Tana's restaurant. That was also the restaurant where Glenn came up with the idea for the "Lyin' Eyes" song. Don recalls, "I don't recall being there on the specific night that Glenn came up with that phrase or title, but I know that his observations were made at Dan Tana's restaurant. It was a great place to people watch,

especially the bar area. There was always some kind of intrigue going on in that place."

14. True. Because it was a soft tune and had been recorded by the band's fired producer, Glenn hesitated before allowing the song to be released as a single. However, several radio stations played the song on heavy rotation and basically forced the record company's hand. Most notably, it was a massive hit on WKMI-AM in Kalamazoo, Michigan. Asylum Records released 1,000 copies of the single in the area, and they sold very quickly.

15. True. Asylum Records made a cut of the song for the single version, which the band detested. The band's manager, Irving Azoff, sent a golden record back to Geffen's company, labeled the "Golden Hacksaw Award."

16. The Watergate Scandal. If you listen to the end of the song, you can hear Glenn say "Say Goodnight, Dick" about Nixon. However, Don is not happy with the result. He explained that it "had something to do with politics, more specifically with the Watergate scandal. But it was a pretty clumsy, incoherent attempt. It was

supposed to be an R&B-type song, but we missed the mark ...We were still learning the ropes in terms of songwriting."

17. Tanqueray. Producer Bill Szymczyk's favorite drink was Tanqueray 'n tonic, which got the band in the spirits to sing the backing vocals.

18. Tom Waits. Glenn really wanted to play the song. He explained, "It's such a car thing. Your first car is like your first apartment. You had a mobile studio apartment! 'Ol' '55' was so Southern California, and yet there was some Detroit in it as well. It was that car thing, and I loved the idea of driving home at sunrise, thinking about what had happened the night before." Unfortunately, Tom was not a fan of the version or the band. Waits said, "not that particularly crazy about (their) rendition of it ... I thought their version was a little antiseptic." In another interview, he went even further: "I don't like the Eagles. They're about as exciting as watching paint dry. Their albums are good for keeping the dust off your turntable, and that's about all."

19. 300,000. The show was billed as the "Woodstock of

the West." The other acts included Black Sabbath, Emerson, Lake & Palmer, Deep Purple and Earth, Wind & Fire.

20. The birth of his son.

DID YOU KNOW

- "Desperado" was a concept album. It was loosely based on the idea that the lifestyles of modern rock stars are not that different from those of outlaws in the wild west. Henley and Frey came up with the concept and brought it to maturation. Leadon and Meisner were not all that interested in the loose idea. Therefore, they allowed Henley and Frey to take control of most of the writing chores. The duo would never relinquish control of the writing again.

- Although "Desperado" was a concept album, the band did not plan it out in advance. They went into the studio with only the most basic outline. As Don explains, "I think we may have had the title song completed, and we had "Outlaw Man," which was a David Blue composition, but we made a lot of the album up as we went along. There was tremendous pressure on us, but I think we got the whole thing done in about three or four weeks. Adding to the difficulty was the fact that we were in London in February. I remember going out into the street to get some fresh air and calm my nerves, but it was freezing out there."

- The band was signed to Asylum Records. However, Atlantic was in charge of distribution. They were quite unhappy with "Desperado," which they did not see as a worthy follow-up to the debut album. Don says, "A guy named Jerry Greenberg was, at that time, the president of Atlantic Records, which was the distributor of the label we were on. When he heard the album, he reportedly put his head in his hands and exclaimed, 'Jeez, they've made a fucking cowboy album!', The company was expecting us to give them more hits." Though the album did not sell as much as the eponymous debut, Henley stands by the album today: "the "Desperado" album was not a commercial or even a critical success, but it served its purpose by establishing us as a band that was willing to roll the dice, to take chances artistically, and not just play it safe and do the expected thing. I think that Neil Young had a lot of influence on us in that way, and Bob Dylan, too, because they were always doing the counterintuitive thing, taking the road less traveled."

- "On the Border" is the album where Frey and Henley really took over the band and marginalized the other members. Glyn Johns believes that was a very bad move for the band. The producer explains, "With 'On the Border,' they ran out of material and enthusiasm, and Frey was pissed off with me. I didn't agree with the way he and Henley were trying to take control of the band to the detriment of the other guys, so they had me removed, and they went and got Bill Szymczyk and spent a year making that record, which gives you a bit of a clue. I spent six weeks making the first two albums." Don sees it differently and said, "Glyn thought we were a nice, country-rock, semi-acoustic band, and every time we wanted to rock 'n roll, he could name a thousand British bands that could do it better." Glenn summed up the new era best. "We had more freedom in the studio with Bill." With Johns gone, the band was free to pursue its own direction with little external interference for better or worse.

CHAPTER 4:

"ONE OF THESE NIGHTS"

1. "One of These Nights" was a huge hit and went to No. 1. How many of their albums reached the top spot on the Billboard charts after that?

   a. Two
   b. Three
   c. Four
   d. Five

2. While recording the album, the band lived at 461 Ocean Boulevard. Which artist commemorated that address in their work?

   a. Elton John
   b. David Bowie
   c. The Carpenters
   d. Eric Clapton

3. Which of the tunes on "One of These Nights" is Glenn's favorite Eagles song?

   a. "Lyin' Eyes"

b. "Take It to the Limit"

c. "One of these Nights"

d. "Journey of the Sorcerer"

4. Which song on the album won the Grammy for Best Pop Performance by a duo or group with vocal?

   a. "Lyin' Eyes"

   b. "Take It to the Limit"

   c. "One of These Nights"

   d. "Journey of the Sorcerer"

5. The song "After the Thrill is Gone" is a reference to an old blues song. Who sang the original song which inspired it?

   a. Howlin' Wolf

   b. Muddy Waters

   c. B.B. King

   d. Buddy Guy

6. Which is the only single to feature Meisner on vocals?

   a. "Lyin' Eyes"

   b. "Take It to the Limit"

   c. "One of These Nights"

d. "Journey of the Sorcerer"

7. True or False. The album won a Grammy for album of the year.

8. When the band recorded the album, they were influenced by the band recording next door. Which band was it?

    a. The Rolling Stones
    b. The Bee Gees
    c. Fleetwood Mac
    d. The Allman Brothers Band

9. The song "I Wish You Peace" was co-written by the daughter of which well-known Republican politician?

    a. Richard Nixon
    b. Nelson Rockefeller
    c. Gerald Ford
    d. Ronald Reagan

10. What was the name of the orchestra that performed the strings on "Journey of the Sorcerer?"

    a. The Royal Orchestra of Jupiter
    b. The Royal Martian Orchestra
    c. The Royal Alien Orchestra

d. The Royal Extraterrestrial Orchestra

11. Bernie Leadon left the band after recording the album. He famously poured a drink on Glenn Frey's head as a parting gift. What did he douse Glenn with?

    a. Whisky
    b. Beer
    c. Coca-Cola
    d. Wine

12. True or False. The band didn't want to release their Greatest Hits 1971-1975 album.

13. Which song on the album was the band's first top 40 hit on the country charts?

    a. "Visions"
    b. "Lyin' Eyes"
    c. "After the Thrill is Gone"
    d. "One of These Nights"

14. Who sang the lead vocal on "Lyin' Eyes? "

    a. Bernie Leadon
    b. Randy Meisner
    c. Glenn Frey
    d. Don Felder

15. True or False. After panning most of the Eagles' early work, Rolling Stone gave "One of These Nights" a glowing review.

16. The instrumental "Journey of the Sorcerer" was used as the theme song for which British TV production?

    a. "Peaky Blinders"
    b. "Timeslip"
    c. "Doctor Who"
    d. "Hitchhikers Guide to the Galaxy"

17. The "One of These Nights" tour hit three foreign countries. Which of these countries was not part of the tour?

    a. Australia
    b. New Zealand
    c. Japan
    d. Canada

18. Which artist designed the award-winning cover for "One of These Nights? "

    a. Andy Warhol
    b. Roger Dean
    c. Boyd Elder

d. Ethan Russell

19. The Frey-Henley songwriting partnership had just started to blossom on this album. Aside from the title track, which song on the album was written by the duo?

    a. "Hollywood Waltz"
    b. "Too Many Hands"
    c. "After the Thrill is Gone"
    d. "Take It to the Limit"

20. Who plays the mandolin on "Hollywood Waltz?"

    a. Don Felder
    b. Glenn Frey
    c. Bernie Leadon
    d. Randy Meisner

ANSWERS

1. C- Four. Indeed, they only released four studio albums after this, and they all hit No.1.

2. D- Eric Clapton. His classic 1974 album was named "461 Ocean Boulevard" because he stayed there while recording it. You can see the property on both the front and back of the album. Felder said, "We spent more time in Miami, in Florida than in California. So, it should really be, 'Welcome to the Hotel Miami or Coconut Grove.'"

3. C- "One of These Nights"

4. A- "Lyin' Eyes"

5. C- B.B. King. Don explains that "We were, of course, aware of B.B. King's song 'The Thrill Is Gone,' which was a straightforward statement. But we wanted to explore the aftermath. We know that the thrill is gone — so, now what?"

6. B- "Take It to the Limit." Randy wrote the song and said, "The line 'take it to the limit' was to keep trying before you reach a point in your life where you feel

you've done everything and seen everything, sort of feeling, you know, part of getting old. And just to take it to the limit one more time, like every day just keep, you know, punching away at it ... So that was the line, and from there, the song took a different course." The fans loved when Randy performed the song live. But Meisner did not like to perform it out of concern that he couldn't hit the high notes.

7. False. But "Lyin' Eyes" won a Grammy for Best Pop Vocal Performance by a Duo, Group, or Chorus.

8. B- The Bee Gees. Don Henley remembers, "Glenn and I had always been fans of the records that were produced in Memphis by Willie Mitchell, especially the Al Green records where the drummer, Al Jackson Jr., would hit the snare and the ride tom-tom at the same time on the backbeat. So, that was a big influence on the title track, but there was also a little nod to disco; we had shared a studio in Miami with the Bee Gees, with the four-on-the-floor bass-drum pattern."

9. Ronald Reagan. His daughter Patti Davis was Bernie Leadon's girlfriend, and she wrote the song with

him. Henley was not a fan of the song and called it "smarmy cocktail music and certainly not something the Eagles are proud of."

10. B- The Royal Martian Orchestra. Since I couldn't find much information on them, I will assume they are actually from Mars.

11. B- Beer. Bernie told Glenn, "You need to chill out, man!" and poured it on him. We are not sure what brand of beer was used.

12. True. They felt that it was premature and a bit embarrassing. Henley said at the time. "Let us say that we aren't really advocates of 'Greatest Hits' albums. They are more or less a ploy by the record company to get free sales. They don't have to spend any money to make them, and they get a lot of money back. We got a couple of hate letters after the 'Greatest Hits' album came out that said we were selling out ... But we didn't have anything to do with it. The record company put it out, and we couldn't stop them. We had a say in picking the tracks, sequencing them, and doing the graphics."

13. B- "Lyin' Eyes." They would not have another top 40 country hit until "How Long" came out in 2007.

14. C- Glenn Frey. The song was Glenn's baby. He later recalled, "The story had always been there. I don't want to say it wrote itself, but once we started working on it, there were no sticking points. Lyrics just kept coming out, and that's not always the way songs get written."

15. False. The album drew a fairly mediocre review. Stephen Holden, a critic with a penchant for writing negative reviews about classic albums, wrote, "For all their worldly perceptiveness, the Eagles' lyrics never transcend Hollywood slickness. Their hard rock has always seemed a bit forced, constructed more from commercial considerations than from any urgent impulse to boogie. And when the Eagles attempt to communicate wild sexuality, they sound only boyishly enthused. These limitations, however, seem built into the latter-day concept of Southern California rock, of which the Eagles remain the unrivaled exponents."

16. D- "Hitchhikers Guide to the Galaxy." The writer of

the book and creator of the show, Douglas Adams, picked the song himself. Adams was a fan and owned the album.

17. Canada. The band kicked off the tour with a show in Auckland, New Zealand, on January 18, 1975. Then they headed to Australia and then Japan before flying to Hawaii and then to mainland USA.

18. Boyd Elder. He did the art covers for this album and their "Greatest Hits" compilation. The band discovered him when they happened to be attending an opening in Venice, California, featuring his work. Designer Gary Burden explained, "The cow skull is pure cowboy, folk, the decorations are American Indian-inspired, and the future is represented by the more polished reflective glass beaded surfaces covering the skull. All set against the dark eagle feather wings that speak of mysterious powers."

19. C- "After The Thrill is Gone"

20. C- Bernie Leadon. The band would miss the multi-instrumental talents of Leadon. However, Felder could play most of the same instruments.

DID YOU KNOW?

- The shared writing process involving Glenn and Don had become very intimate when they recorded "One of These Nights." Don describes it as, "A quiet private space, usually a room with a coffee table, a couple of acoustic guitars and a piano. Maybe some beer or maybe just soft drinks or water. Lots of legal pads and pens. We both contributed music and lyrics. Sometimes Glenn would lead the way; other times, I would, depending on who had come up with an idea — a chord progression, a title, or a theme. But Glenn described the process beautifully in the documentary — time, thought, perseverance, elbow grease, revisions, rewrites." In another interview, Don added that "back then, we were always finishing each other's sentences; we had a kind of telepathy going on. In some ways, the tandem almost worked too well together." That is why Bernie Leadon felt like there was no room for him in the band anymore. The turn towards a more rocking sound was also an issue for Leadon. "Bernie had bluegrass roots," Henley continued. "He'd never really messed with rock 'n roll guitar, and he never really understood how to get that dirty rock 'n roll sound. He was just not schooled or programmed in that area."

- However, there were other reasons that Leadon left the band. He was just tired. Don says, "We knew for two years that Bernie wasn't happy with the road," said Henley. "He'd been doing it longer than the rest of us. He'd been in The Burrito Brothers, remember, and his road map started five or six years before we began traveling at all."

- The large-scale success of the band is even more incredible when you consider that they reached the heights of success in the 1970s. That was the showiest decade imaginable, with big spectacle acts like Kiss and Elton John. Yet, the Eagles refused to participate in that trend. Meisner explains, "We had no intention of being a flashy band; we just wanted the music to come across. Just wanted to concentrate on the music and be the best we could be on stage. I wanted to make sure I sang the right parts, and we were playing the right parts and making that sound that we put on the record. That was our main concern. It wasn't about who was the coolest on stage. We avoided a lot of publicity we actually could have had. It's almost like if you don't give many interviews, they're almost *more* curious about you." He summarizes the image of the band as "we wanted people to think we were just like you. We were just like anybody else."

- Bill believes that recording in Florida was a significant part of the success of "One of These Nights" and "Hotel California." He said, "We'd always get more of a swamp sound in Florida. The best thing about working and living in Florida is it got them out of their hometown, and by doing so, made them a hell of a lot more comfortable. They were in a much more creative, non-hassle environment than in L.A. They wrote more because they were interrupted less."

CHAPTER 5:

"HOTEL CALIFORNIA"

1. True or False. Joe Walsh had long asked for a chance to be in the band. Therefore, when Bernie Leadon left, they finally allowed him to audition.

2. Despite being the ultimate California album, much of "Hotel California" was recorded in Miami. So why did the band record the album on the other side of the country?

   a. To keep away from bad influences
   b. To freshen up the band's sound
   c. Fear of earthquakes
   d. The band loves Miami

3. Which song on the album was written by Randy Meisner?

   a. "Life in the Fast Lane"
   b. "New Kid in Town"
   c. "Wasted Time"
   d. "Try and Love Again"

4. The album was primarily written in the studio. Which was the one song the band had written in advance?

    a. "Life in the Fast Lane"
    b. "New Kid in Town"
    c. "Wasted Time"
    d. "Try and Love Again"

5. The album was painstakingly recorded, with multiple takes and overdubs. Which song bucked the trend and was recorded in one take?

    a. "Victim of Love"
    b. "Life in the Fast Lane"
    c. "Pretty Maids All in a Row"
    d. "Wasted Time"

6. What was the working title of the song "Hotel California?"

    a. "Mexican Reggae"
    b. "Jamaican Flamenco"
    c. "Italian Disco"
    d. "Canadian Rock"

7. The song "Hotel California" includes a nod to another legendary '70s band. Which band received a sly tribute?

   a. Fleetwood Mac

   b. Steely Dan

   c. Kiss

   d. Crosby, Stills, and Nash

8. When and where was the famous solo on "Hotel California" written?

   a. In the studio

   b. In Don's house in Malibu

   c. At a hotel in Miami

   d. On the road

9. True or False. Don Felder worked on the song "Hotel California" for months before all the parts finally came together.

10. True or False. Randy Meisner left the band because Glenn and Don would not let him take a more central role.

11. When recording in Miami, another band was recording next door. They were so loud that

recording had to be stopped on more than one occasion. Who were the noisy neighbors?

   a. Black Sabbath

   b. Deep Purple

   c. Judas Priest

   d. Led Zeppelin

12. True or False. There are several unreleased songs and outtakes from the "Hotel California" sessions.

13. True or False. The band was on so many drugs that they were miserable when they recorded "Hotel California." They were surprised that such a successful album came out of such a difficult period.

14. The album's front cover is a famous shot of the Beverly Hills Hotel, shot just before sunset. Where was the back cover shot?

   a. The Roosevelt

   b. The Biltmore

   c. The Lido

   d. The Chateau Marmont

15. The "Hotel California" cover was designed by the art director known as Kosh. What is his most famous

album cover design?

   a. "Dark Side of the Moon"

   b. "Led Zeppelin IV"

   c. "Abbey Road"

   d. "The Velvet Underground & Nico"

16. True or False. The Beverly Hills Hotel threatened to sue for unlicensed use of the hotel on the album cover.

17. The first single from the album went to No. 1 on the Billboard charts. Which song was the inaugural chart-topper?

   a. "Life in the Fast Lane"

   b. "New Kid in Town"

   c. "Hotel California"

   d. "Victim of Love"

18. After "Hotel California," there was talk of an Eagles live album. Why wasn't it recorded in the end?

   a. Copyright and licensing problems

   b. The band shows at the time were not very good

   c. The band disliked live albums

   d. The band's shows were not significantly

different from the albums

19. True or False. "Hotel California" was the highest-selling album of the 20th Century in the U.S.

20. True or False. "Hotel California" won both Best Record and Best Album at the 1978 Grammy Awards.

ANSWERS

1. False. Joe had been friends with the band but had no firm plans to join the band. However, Don said, "We had talked to Joe as early as the beginning of 1975, and his attitude was that ... 'If it ever happens, give me a call.' He'd spent a lot of time in his solo ballpark, but he also knew what it was like to be in a band. So, we more or less knew which way things were going to go, and it was more or less a matter of time."

2. C- Fear of earthquakes. Namely, producer Bill Szymczyk had developed a fear of a big earthquake. Naturally, therefore, he vastly preferred to record in Miami.

3. C- "Try and Love Again." They had bits and pieces of the other songs. However, they were all put together during the recording process. Producer Bill Szymczyk recalls, "At that point, it had become the norm. With "On the Border," all the songs were pretty much done. "In One of These Nights, "three songs were done. The rest were made up in the

studio. [In] "Hotel California," there was one." Don has a more jaded view. He said, "When we began the process of recording that album, we were completely burned out. We were physically, emotionally, spiritually, and creatively exhausted. Our collective tank was empty. We'd been touring relentlessly, even in between recording sessions. We should have taken a one-year hiatus, but the Big Machine demanded to be fed. Momentum had to be maintained. There were big bucks at stake; the corporate stockholders had expectations; jobs were on the line."

4. D- "Try and Love Again." Randy remembers, "That was the last song I wrote for the band. Joe (Walsh) helped me a little bit with that. I had that song for a long time and never really got it finished. I brought it in for those album sessions, we worked on it and worked on it, and it turned out really good. Don and Glenn helped put it together."

5. A- "Victim of Love." Bill recalls, "Everything on there, except the vocals, was done live at the same time, lead guitar and everything. There's always a

lead guitar overdub or extra acoustics or things like that. This would be the only one. We listened and decided that's pretty fucking good like it is."

6. A- "Mexican Reggae." At first, a strange-sounding sound played in a higher key with more of a fast reggae beat. Felder recalls that Henley "sounded like Barry Gibb in this high voice." So, they lowered the key from E minor to B minor, "which is not a particularly guitar-friendly key, but it was perfect for his voice."

7. B- Steely Dan. The line in question is: "They stab it with their steely knives, but they just can't kill the beast." Frey explained, "One of the things that impressed us about Steely Dan was that they would say anything in their songs, and it didn't have to necessarily make sense. They called it joke sculpture." That was part of the inspiration for the "Hotel California" lyrics. Glenn says, "We're sort of trying to expand our lyrical horizons and just take on something in the realm of the bizarre, as Steely Dan had done."

8. B- In Don's house in Malibu. Felder and Walsh tried

to write it in the studio. But Henley stopped them and said that it was better in the demo. Felder recalls, "The only problem was, I did that demo a year earlier; I couldn't even remember what was on it. So, we had to call my housekeeper in Malibu, who took the cassette, put it in a ghetto blaster, and played it with the phone held up to the blaster. Then, we recorded it, and I had to sit in Miami and play exactly what was on the demo."

9. False. It came to Don in a flash. He remembers, "At the time, I was living in a rental beach house on Malibu Beach, and I had two little kids. One was about a year old; one was about 2.5 years old. And I was sitting on the couch one day just playing an acoustic guitar and looking out at the sun glistening on the Pacific Ocean, and watching my two kids playing in the sand and this little swing set we had on the beach. And out came that progression two or three times, and I — I had to go record a little bit of it so I wouldn't forget it. So, I went back and recorded that little progression three or four times, and turned it off, and went out and played with my

kids on the beach."

10. False. Randy insists that, "I liked to be on the side and play and do my parts. I was kind of shy, actually. I just wanted to do my job." When it comes to new material, he says that was never a problem either. "Everybody was welcome to write a song. I didn't write as much, that's all." Don and Glenn were a team, and they had a good thing going. I was basically on my own. I'd bring in a song, and they'd tell me if they liked it." The problem was that his family was in Nebraska, and he barely saw them. Randy remembers, "It just was hard, they lived in Nebraska, and they didn't want to move to L.A. That was kinda tough going through that, and it affected me on the road. It's one of the reasons I left the Eagles."

11. A- Black Sabbath. The British heavy metal pioneers were recording the album "Technical Ecstasy" at Criteria Studios, Miami. In particular, the loud neighbors interrupted the recording of the song "Last Resort."

12. False. The band does not have a lot of unused songs in the vaults. Don explains, "We can usually tell

when we start a song that if we get past an eighth of the way into finishing it, it'll be worth doing. If we don't get that far, then we know it won't be worth finishing. The ones that get finished wind up on the record. I know some people write a lot of tunes, pick the best and throw the rest away, but with us, they never reach that far. We do save ideas, though, especially ballads. We also try to balance an album because we believe it's a work of art, and it should have contrast and continuity at the same time."

13. False. The band was having a great time and knew that this would be a very successful album. Don recalls that there was a tension between some of the darker themes on the album and the joy they were experiencing by making the album. "They're the same themes that run through all of our work: loss of innocence, the cost of naiveté, the perils of fame, of excess; exploration of the dark underbelly of the American dream, idealism realized and idealism thwarted, illusion versus reality, the difficulties of balancing loving relationships and work, trying to square the conflicting relationship between business

and art; the corruption in politics, the fading away of the Sixties' dream of peace, love, and understanding. But it's also important to remember that during the making of the "Hotel California" album, we were ecstatic much of the time. We knew we were onto something. So, you have the interesting juxtaposition of dark themes being developed and constructed in an atmosphere of excitement and productivity."

14. C- Now a humble apartment building, the Lido was a well-loved Hollywood hotel back in the day. William Holden's character tells Gloria Swanson that he lives there in the classic movie "Sunset Boulevard." Henley says he choose that hotel for its atmosphere. "I wanted a collection of people from all walks of life; it's people on the edge, on the fringes of society."

15. C- "Abbey Road." Kosh remembers, "Don wanted me to find and portray *the* "Hotel California" – and portray it with a slightly sinister edge." Kosh and photographer David Alexander stood for hours on a platform, waiting for the sun to set behind the

Beverly Hills Hotel and hit the building at the right angle. Alexander later said, "Very few people who even know the Beverly Hills Hotel knew that it was the Beverly Hills Hotel. We were in the business of creating fantasies. And that's what it is."

16. True. Kosh recalls, "As sales went through the roof, lawyers for the Beverly Hills Hotel threatened me with a cease-and-desist action. Until it was gently pointed out by my attorney that the hotel's requests for bookings had tripled since the release of their album."

17. B- "New Kid in Town." The J.D. Souther song struck a chord with its meditation on an eternal theme of life. In addition, he said, the song is about how "at some point, some kid would come riding into town that was much faster than you, and he'd say so, and then he'd prove it. So, we were just writing about our replacements."

18. D- The band's shows were not very different from the albums. While many bands at that time performed wildly different versions of their songs live, the Eagles did not, and it was not clear what a live album would

add to their canon. Bill says, "Other people's live albums sound quite a bit different from the records. That's not the case with the Eagles. They'd go out of their way to recreate the album cut. So, they weren't drastically different."

19. False. To the band's surprise, the compilation album "Their Greatest Hits (1971–1975)" became their highest-selling album and the biggest-selling album in U.S. history. It became the first album to receive the RIAA Platinum Certification. It was only surpassed by Michael Jackson's "Thriller" in 2009. The album has been classified and stored by the National Recording Registry by the Library of Congress as being "culturally, historically, or artistically significant." Despite being important elements in those songs, Randy Meisner said neither he nor Bernie Leadon was notified of the band's award in 1999 when it became the biggest-selling album of the century. Meisner said, "We had to call, and we finally received it."

20. False. While the Eagles won Best Record for the title song, they lost the Best Album award to their rivals

Fleetwood Mac. The band also won the best arrangement for their work on "New Kid in Town."

DID YOU KNOW

- "Hotel California" has one of the most famous guitar solos in rock history. It is particularly notable for the interplay between the guitarists. How did the musical communication between the two guitarists get so good? Don and Joe Walsh had been playing together for a while before the latter joined the band. So, Don knew his style very well. When he wrote the music to "Hotel California," Felder designed it as a canvass for interweaving dual guitar parts. Don remembers, "That was conscious and aimed at trying to have a — a bed that we can do that on. So, I — when I got to the part where I was recreating or making up or adlibbing these solos, I said I'd play something kind of like this, and Joe had played something kind of like this, and then I'd play this, and he'd play something like that. And so, I made a little mix of that, I think, 14 or 15 other song ideas; one became "Victim of Love," and put it on this cassette and made copies of the cassette." The interplay between the guitarists was inspired by Eric Clapton and Duane Allman's work on the song "Layla." Felder says, "It was just — it was something that all guitar players like to do, to go together against somebody that plays really well, and it pushes you up to another level. And so, I wanted to do that with Joe on this record, so I kind of designed that whole track with that in mind." Walsh says the solo was a collaborative effort. Joe said, "the lead parts that we trade-off, he came up with his, I came up with mine. And the stuff that we played together was worked out together."

- Everyone has a theory as to what the song "Hotel California" is about. The most popular idea is that it is a metaphor for the hedonism of the '70s. And in interviews, the members have usually been reluctant to explain the exact meaning behind the lyrics. But if you study the lyric sheet and the explanations Henley and Frey have given, it may not really have a clear intention. Instead, it is a series of evocative images open to the interpretation of the listener. Glenn once said in an interview, "Everybody wants to know what that song was about, and we don't know." Another time he explained, "All of our songs were cinematic, but we wanted to open up with a montage. It was just one shot to the next — a picture of a guy on the highway, a picture of the hotel, the guy walks in, the door opens, strange people. We take this guy and make him like a character in "The Magus," where every time he walks through a door, there's a new version of reality. We decided to create something strange, just to see if we could do it. And then a lot was read into it — a lot more than probably exists. I think we achieved perfect ambiguity." And there is the secret. The song evokes people's imaginations because they can interpret it as they wish.

- There are many theories and rumors about satanic messages in the "Hotel California" song and album. One rumor is that late Church of Satan founder Anton LaVey is standing in one of the hotel windows on the album cover. Joe denies this vehemently. "Absolutely not. Any reference to Satan or anything like that is completely in the eyes of whoever is thinking that. That's a reflection of how sick they are. The guy in the window is one of the Elektra/Asylum publicity guys. The lighting just happened to be bad, and he was really shy, so he was just peeking around the corner."

- "Hotel California" turned the Eagles into the biggest band in the world, at least for a while. Like any band with that level of success, the guys struggled to keep themselves grounded. At the time, Don said, "What he means by that," attempting to introduce an element of seriousness into an interview that had already lasted well over an hour, "is that especially over the past year, we have felt a tremendous amount of pressure. It's almost harder once you get to the top of the mountain than it is climbing it. It's hard to stay up there and maintain it. I admire the Stones, no matter what I think about their music, because they've stuck there. I admire Paul Simon and The Who simply because they've stuck around and not burned themselves out. It's hard because you lose a lot of friends along the way." However, Don also added that the success had been a blessing, and "we asked for it." But like any peak, afterward, there is nowhere to go but down. Don said, "I think that we were at the height of our powers. Every band has a peak, and that was ours. And because of various factors — pressure to perform at peak level, pressure to deliver more of the same, the changing nature of the band dynamic, the constantly changing public tastes, etc. — it was impossible for us to take time off that we needed in order to get our heads together, to regain a sense of perspective that we had lost."

• How big were the Eagles? Don has an amusing anecdote about that: "I was once visiting a remote village in a mountaintop jungle in Honduras — and when I say remote, I mean these people were living in the most primitive of conditions — no electricity, no plumbing; crude, makeshift shelters — when one of the villagers disappeared into a little hut and came out holding a beat-up old cassette player. He pointed to the cassette player, then pointed at me. I later found out that the cassette in the player was "Hotel California." The song got around."

CHAPTER 6:

"THE LONG RUN"

1. True or False. Timothy B. Schmitt replaced Randy Meisner as a member of Poco before replacing him in the Eagles as well.

2. True or False. One of the reasons the band broke up is because "The Long Run" was a commercial failure.

3. When the band went into the studio to record "The Long Run," how many of the songs on the album had been written in advance?

    a. None
    b. Three
    c. Five
    d. All the songs on the album

4. The band recorded a song called "You're Really High, Aren't You?" which sadly did not make the final cut. Who wrote the song?

    a. Don Felder
    b. Don Henley

c. Glenn Frey

d. Joe Walsh

5. How long did it take to record "The Long Run" album?

   a. One year

   b. One-and-a-half years

   c. Two years

   d. Two-and-a-half years

6. Which song on "The Long Run" reached No. 1 on the charts?

   a. "The Long Run"

   b. "King of Hollywood"

   c. "Heartache Tonight"

   d. "I Can't Tell You Why"

7. Which song on the album was a tribute to Glenn's Michigan garage rock past?

   a. "King of Hollywood"

   b. "In the City"

   c. "Heartache Tonight"

   d. "The Greeks Don't Want No Freaks"

8. The song "The Sad Café" was written about which

iconic L.A. spot?

    a. The Sunset Grill

    b. The Troubadour

    c. Coles

    d. Musso & Frank Grill

9. One of the catalysts for the band's breakup was the behavior of Don Felder in a benefit concert for a Senator. Who was the Senator in question?

    a. Alan Cranston

    b. John Tunney

    c. Barbara Boxer

    d. Dianne Feinstein

10. Who initiated the breakup of the band in 1980?

    a. Glenn Frey

    b. Don Henley

    c. Joe Walsh

    d. Don Felder

11. After the band had already decided to break up, Elektra Records had them release a live album. However, it needed vocal harmony touch-ups. So, what did the band do?

a. They released the album warts and all

b. The whole band got back together in the studio

c. Frey and Henley got in the studio without Felder

d. They completed the album by mail

12. Amazingly, one of the songs on "Eagles Live" was recorded at the catastrophic show that broke the band up. Which song was it?

    a. "Take it to the Limit"

    b. "Hotel California"

    c. "Life in the Fast Lane"

    d. "The Long Run"

13. Which song on Don Henley's solo album "Can't Stand Still" was criticized for being "un-American?"

    a. "Them and Us"

    b. "Dirty Laundry"

    c. "Johnny Can't Read"

    d. "Long Way Home"

14. Don Henley's biggest hit was the "Boys of Summer." The original recording of it was changed in a way that made it more appealing before its release. What

change was made in the second version?

a. The addition of electric drums

b. The pitch was shifted

c. The chorus was rewritten

d. The synthesizers were added

15. Who directed the excellent music video for the "Boys of Summer?"

a. Marcello Anciano

b. Steve Barron

c. Jean-Baptiste Mondino

d. Marty Callner

16. The solo on Don's song "Sunset Grill" was played on a synthesizer. What instrument was it originally written for?

a. Trumpet

b. French horn

c. Flute

d. Trombone

17. Don Henley filled in on drums for a band at the Video Music Awards. Which band was it?

a. Metallica

b. Guns N' Roses

c. Nirvana

d. Soundgarden

18. Joe Walsh has had a pretty successful solo career. Which of his solo albums (not including those made with Barnstorm) made the top 10 on the Billboard album charts?

    a. "So What"

    b. "You Can't Argue With a Sick Mind"

    c. "But, Seriously Folks … "

    d. "There Goes the Neighborhood"

19. Glenn Frey had a smash hit with the "Heat is On, " released in 1984. Which movie did the song appear on?

    a. Red Dawn

    b. Revenge of the Nerds

    c. Beverly Hills Cop

    d. Romancing the Stone

20. Glenn's song, "Smugglers Blues," inspired an episode in a TV show. They even invited him to guest star in it. Which show was it?

a. "TJ Hooker"

b. "Miami Vice"

c. "21 Jump Street"

d. "Cagney & Lacey"

ANSWERS

1. True. But Meisner does not hold a grudge against his twice-over replacement. On the contrary, Randy says, "He just keeps followin' me around. Really nice guy. I mean, at the Hall of Fame, he made such a nice remark — you know, just givin' me all the best, and telling people 'Randy's done most of all this work' and he's just so honest and so nice!"

2. False. The album reached No. 1 in the Billboard charts and sold 7 million. Sure, nothing was going to top "Hotel California," but this was a very successful album.

3. A- None. The band felt utterly emptied by the process of recording "Hotel California" and had not been writing at all. That is one of the reasons recording took so long; the songs had to be developed from scratch. Producer Bill Szymczyk said, "Everyone came in with a little. Mostly it was Felder and Walsh and Glenn saying, 'I've got this chord change, I've got this chorus.' We just started stacking up these incredible tracks with no words. After 18 tracks,

maybe we should write some words! Then, when push came to shove, all of this in 18 months, the label was freaking out."

4. A- Don Felder. Felder remembers, "I actually wrote a couple of things for "The Long Run," one of which we didn't finish. It was sort of a harder rock song. I got a call in the early '80s for the movie *Heavy Metal*. I took this track I'd written and recorded for the Eagles that Joe and I were going to do." Why did the song have that amusing name? Producer Bill Szymczyk recalls, "That was one of the left-off 18 tracks. I remember it because of the title. That's what Joe said to him when we recorded this. It just never got finished."

5. B- One-and-a-half years. That was the longest it had ever taken them to record an album. There is a reason they called it "The Long Run!" No one remembers it fondly. Joe says about the recording sessions, "Those were brutal. Those were brutal. We were touring at the same time we were in the studio. When we took a break from touring, we were in the studio. When we had to take a break from that, we

went on the road. It just kept going crazy like that."

6. C- "Heartache Tonight." It was to be the final chart-topper for the band before they broke up. Two other singles from the album made the top 10.

7. D- "The Greeks Don't Want No Freaks." As Don explains, "It had the cheesy Farfisa organ and garbled, partially incoherent lyrics in the mode of "Louie Louie," the 1963 hit by the Kingsmen, another frat favorite. Playing those frat parties was another dues-paying experience. We witnessed a little bit of everything."

8. B- The Troubadour. Don waxed nostalgically, "We could feel an era passing. The crowd that hung out in the Troubadour and the bands that were performing there were changing. The train tracks that had run down the middle of Santa Monica Boulevard had been ripped out. The train no longer came through — the same train that Steve Martin had once led an entire Troubadour audience to hop aboard and ride up to La Cienega Boulevard, then walk back to the club. Those remarkable freewheeling times were receding into the distance."

9. A- Alan Cranston. The band agreed to perform a benefit for the incumbent California Senator. However, when Senator Cranston came backstage to thank the band, Glenn says that Felder did not give the elected official the due amount of respect. Instead, Frey recalls, that Felder said, "You're welcome, Senator … I guess." As a result, Glenn felt Don Felder insulted Senator Cranston under his breath, and Glenn confronted him with it. A legendary backstage brawl involving punched walls and broken beer bottles took place as a result.

10. A- Glenn Frey. Don says that "he was a very dynamic individual … The way the group broke up was Glenn called me up, and he said, 'I need to go and do my own thing for a while,' you know. And — and that was it." Don says he replied, "Okay, whatever."

11. D- They completed the album by mail. Bill recalls, "We were fixing three-part harmonies courtesy of Federal Express." As a result of all the overdubs, the *Rolling Stone Album Guide* referred to it as "perhaps the most heavily overdubbed live album in history."

12. C- "Life in the Fast Lane. Even the song choice was ironic.

13. C- "Johnny Can't Read." The song criticizes American culture in a very biting manner. Don believes that is one of the reasons the album didn't do well. He said, "'Johnny Can't Read' was the wrong thing to do. It was a little bit too much of a leftfield turn from the Eagles days, and it took a lot of people by surprise. It was too controversial. It pissed people off. There was a DJ in Houston who wouldn't play it. A DJ in Atlanta said it was *un-American!* And it hit home to too many people who couldn't read, you know? And football in America is right up there with God!"

14. B- The pitch was shifted. Namely, the producers upped the pitch to add an element of drama to the song. It works and adds drama to the excellent lyrics. Don's sighting of a Cadillac inspired the song with a Grateful Dead sticker on it, an incident mentioned in the song. Henley recalled, "I was driving down the San Diego Freeway and got passed by a $21,000 Cadillac Seville, the status symbol of the right-wing upper-middle-class American bourgeoisie — all the

guys with the blue blazers with the crests and the grey pants — and there was this Grateful Dead "Deadhead" bumper sticker on it!"

15. C- Jean-Baptiste Mondino. Mondino explained why he took the job: "I was living in Paris, and we were into a new era, more modern. But I couldn't refuse to go to LA — it was like a dream. When I got there, I was very disappointed because there's a big difference between what I saw when I was a kid in the beautiful old Hollywood movies and what LA's actually about. When I listened to Boys of Summer, there was something nostalgic — he was looking back, talking about something that he's leaving behind. The '70s were dying."

16. D- Trombone. The trombonist couldn't get the sound he wanted, so guitarist Danny Kortchmar played it on the synth. Incidentally, the legendary Randy Newman helped program the synths on that album.

17. B- Guns N' Roses. Their drummer Steven Adler was experiencing severe drug dependence problems. Therefore, Don generously agreed to step in for his fellow California band. He remembers, "I played

with them on the American Music Awards, just for a laugh. It confused a lot of people. Those guys were a mess."

18. C- "But, Seriously, Folks … " The album was a massive hit, mostly on the back of the single "Life's Been Good." Some dismissed the song as a hollow boast about Joe's success. However, Walsh disagrees. He explained, "I wanted to make a statement involving satire and humor, kind of poking fun at the incredibly silly lifestyle that someone in my position is faced with — in other words, I do have a really nice house, but I'm on the road so much that when I come home from a tour, it's really hard to feel that I even live here. It's not necessarily me, I think it paraphrases anyone in my position, and I think that's why a lot of people related to it, but basically, that's the story of any rock star — I say that humbly — anyone in my position. I thought that was a valid statement because it is a strange lifestyle."

19. C- *Beverly Hills Cop*. The song reached No. 2 on the charts and was helped by the success of the Eddie Murphy movie. He was very happy to have a song in

that movie. Glenn recalls, "The Eagles are broken up, and it's in the middle '80s, and Irving Azoff, my manager, calls me up and said, 'Glenn, you got to come to a screening. We're going to show this movie, this Eddie Murphy movie. It's going to be huge. You've got to get a song in it. Come on.' So I went to the screening, and I'm sitting there, and Don was there, and Irving was there, and we're waiting for the movie to start, and I look over my shoulder — Quincy Jones. Okay. I look over my shoulder — Stevie Wonder. Look back over here; it's the Pointer Sisters. I'm sitting there going, 'I'm dead. There's no way I'm getting a song in *Beverly Hills Cop*.'" He remembered thinking to himself, "This movie is going to be huge." But I never thought I'd get a song in it. So, a month or two goes by, and then all of a sudden, somebody says, "Hey, we're going to send you a song. See if you maybe want to sing it. It's written by these guys, Keith Forsey and Harold Faltermeyer; the guys in Munich that do the Donna Summer records are going to send you something. See if you want to sing it." So, they sent me a demo of "The Heat is On." It sounded kind of like a Huey Lewis thing, the saxophone in it. Kind of sounded like something I might do. So, I said, 'Okay, I'll do it' So, I met the guys, I came in, I sang it one day, I played guitar and did background vocals the next day, and I got a small check I think 15 grand. I had a little Christmas money, and I was happy."

20. B- *Miami Vice*. If you listen to the visceral lyrics, it is clear why. For example, the lines: "I knew the gun was loaded/But I didn't think he'd kill/Everything exploded, and the blood began to spill." Glenn was very successful in the '80s and tied many of his songs to '80s pop culture. For example, he licensed his song, "You Belong to the City to Pepsi." This led to accusations from some musicians that Frey had sold out. His defense was interesting; Glenn said, "If Little Steven and Neil Young don't like me doing Pepsi commercials, I trade insults at 40 paces. When has integrity ever been synonymous with rock 'n roll?"

DID YOU KNOW?

- By all accounts, recording "The Long Run" was a very unpleasant experience. Part of it was simply a lack of inspiration. Glenn remembered, "It had stopped being fun, we no longer trusted each other's instincts, so there was considerable disagreement. Plus, both Henley and I had developed drug habits, which didn't help matters. Going to the studio was like going to school — I simply didn't want to go. But most importantly, during the making of "The Long Run," Henley and I found out that lyrics are not a replenishable source. We, Don, in particular, said a mouthful on "Hotel California," and a big part of the problem was wondering, 'what do we talk about now?' Towards the end, we just wanted to get the record finished and released. It is a very polished album, as well it should be after all that, and has some excellent moments, but none of us wanted to go through that again." Producer Bill Szymczyk summed it up, "I agree 100 percent. It was a bitch. There was the constant pressure of topping "Hotel California," which in retrospect was a big row to hoe. There was a lot of angst from everybody. It led to the most nitpicked album I've ever worked on."

- Don was dating Stevie Nicks from Fleetwood Mac as he tried to come up with the follow-up to "Hotel California." Nicks was going through a similar process. Her band, Fleetwood Mac, was attempting to follow up the massively successful "Rumors." That resulted in "Tusk," which was a long and only partially successful [successor] to the previous smash, much like "The Long Run." Henley recalls, "We were in a dark place. We were doing way too many drugs, just fucked up all the time because we felt this tremendous pressure. We should have taken a year off or hired a band psychiatrist. Or both." The dating between members of the band created an intense and unhealthy rivalry between the two supergroups. Producer Bill Szymczyk was all too aware of this dynamic. He said, "Yeah, we were in some serious competition with Fleetwood Mac at the time. It was two big albums, fighting it out with the other biggest band of the time. The competition between Fleetwood Mac and the Eagles originated from "Rumors" and "Hotel California." We were both working on those albums at the same time." The competition led to the decision to make "The Long Run" a double album. Bill says, "They went in the studio first and made it known they were going to make a double album. That was like throwing down the gauntlet. Then, of course, Don and Glenn, being the competitors that they are, said we're going to do a double album, too."

- They finally managed to overcome the pressure by resisting the urge to make a massive statement. Joe explains, "The Long Run was a pretty painful birth because we were like, how the fuck are we going to top 'Hotel California'? This is useless. We finally got over that and just made another album where we all played together in the same room. And that was 'The Long Run.'"

- In 1979 Don was arrested for "contributing to the delinquency of a minor." A 16-year-old girl suffered a drug overdose at one of his parties. The police raided the house and found a considerable stash of cocaine and quaaludes. They also found a good amount of marijuana, which was still illegal in those simpler times.

- Don Felder and Glenn Frey were experiencing extreme tensions when the band broke up. Frey said to Felder in their last show together, "I'm gonna kill you. I can't wait." Joe remembers that it was never easy to record with the guys in the band. He said the best thing you can do is, "Just smile and nod. They're just real alpha guys in the band. We've always been strong personalities, and we're all solo artists." But the tensions were also the band's strength. He explained, "Some of the tension between us has been really good creatively. We don't fight so much anymore; we agree to disagree. When we're together — and we know this — it becomes something much bigger than any of us individually. There's something special about the band, and we know that."

- Henley's excellent debut album, "I Can't Stand Still," came out when the Asylum record label was experiencing a major shakeup. For that reason, it never got the exposure it needed. Don recalls, "They fired about 500 people one week and brought in this guy Bob Krasnow, who, I guess, is a nice guy (*pregnant pause*), and they moved the company to New York. And Krasnow made some comments to the press about 'all the old dinosaurs we have on the label,' and it really pissed me and Frey off. They started signing all kinds of acts, from Tony Orlando & Dawn to Pink Lady … I looked at a roster in the late Seventies, and there were 80 or 90 acts, and I think I recognized about five of them — and, of course, we were paying for all that."

CHAPTER 7:

LOSS AND REBIRTH

1. In 1993, an Eagles tribute album named "Common Thread: The Songs of the Eagles" was released by Giant Records. Who covered "Take It Easy" on the album?

    a. Travis Titt

    b. Garth Brooks

    c. Jackson Browne

    d. Vince Gill

2. The band's reunion tour was called Hell Freezes Over. Which member of the band inspired the name?

    a. Don Henley

    b. Joe Walsh

    c. Glenn Frey

    d. Don Felder

3. The live album "When Hell Freezes Over" included four new songs. Which one was released as a single?

    a. "Get Over It"

b. "Love Will Keep Us Alive"

c. "The Girl from Yesterday"

d. "Learn to be Still"

4. How many years passed between the recording of "The Long Run" and the band's next studio album, "Long Road Out of Eden?"

   a. 19 years

   b. 23 years

   c. 28 years

   d. 31 years

5. Which member parted ways with the band right before the recording of "Long Road Out of Eden?"

   a. Joe Walsh

   b. Don Felder

   c. Timothy B. Schmitt

   d. Vince Gill

6. The band started recording the "Long Road Out of Eden" with long-time producer Bill Szymczyk. Why did they finish the album without him?

   a. Musical differences

   b. Personal differences

c. Bill's health

d. Glenn and Don wanted to produce

7. The rest of the band appreciated Henley's lyrics expertise greatly. But they would sometimes teasingly call him by what nickname?

    a. The lyrics guru

    b. The lyrics fascist

    c. The lyrical poet

    d. The lyrics police

8. Glenn Frey also had an interesting nickname. Other members called him …

    a. The lone arranger

    b. The arranger stranger

    c. The poser composer

    d. Our fearless leader

9. True or False. Don was delighted with Frank Ocean's sampling of "Hotel California" on his 2011 mixtape "Nostalgia, Ultra."

10. True or False. The Eagles have always looked down on hit singles and considered themselves an album band despite having many hits.

11. Which famous drummer is Joe Walsh's brother-in-law?

   a. Keith Moon
   b. John Bonham
   c. Ringo Starr
   d. Ginger Baker

12. True or False. Stevie Nicks has described Don Henley as the "love of her life."

13. True or False. Joe Walsh says he is completely sick of hearing "Hotel California."

14. True or False. The band hates being considered a nostalgia act.

15. True or False. When Glenn died, Henley said the band would never get back together.

16. As a young journalist Cameron Crowe wrote a cover story about the Eagles for *Rolling Stone*. They returned the favor by playing on one of his movies as solo artists. Which movie featured several members of the Eagles?

   a. Fast Times at Ridgemont High
   b. Say Anything

c. The Wildlife

d. Almost Famous

17. Which member did the band snub when they were inducted into the Rock and Roll Hall of Fame?

a. Randy Meisner

b. Bernie Leadon

c. Don Felder

d. Timothy B. Schmitt

18. True or False. Don Felder sued the band after its successful "Hell Freezes Over" tour.

19. Which member unexpectedly returned to the lineup for the "History of the Eagles" tour.

a. Randy Meisner

b. Bernie Leadon

c. Don Felder

d. Timothy B. Schmitt

20. In 2016, Glenn died in New York, leaving the band bereaved and in disarray. Deacon Frey replaced him. How is he related to Glenn?

a. His brother

b. His cousin

c. His son

d. His grandson

ANSWERS

1. A- Travis Titt. That was also the single from the album, and Travis asked the band to join him in filming the video. It turned out to be an important step in getting the band back together. Glenn remembers, "After years passed, you really sort of remember that you were friends first ... I just remembered how much we genuinely had liked each other and how much fun we'd had."

2. A- Don Henley. He had famously said that the band would get back together "when hell freezes over."

3. A- "Get Over It." The fun song hit No. 31 on the charts and includes a sly reference to William Shakespeare.

4. C- 28 years. Being away for so long meant the band had a dilemma on how to move ahead. Henley explained, "It's tricky at this stage of the game. We're 30 years on here, and we're known for all that stuff in the '70s. So, it's going to be tricky to be who we are and yet be contemporary. It's a fine line. We

don't want to sound like we're trying too hard to be trendy, and we don't want to sound antiquated either. So, it's like walking a tightrope."

5. B- Don Felder. The guitarist had a long history of not getting along with the other members. Henley preferred not to explain exactly what happened but said, "I'll say this. It's something that's been coming for quite a long time. There has been unrest for many years now, and it finally got to the point where it was intolerable. And the new Eagles — I think the band will be more creative. And that's about all I can say right now. I could go on a complete rant, but ..."

6. D- Glenn and Don wanted to produce. Henley explained, "We actually began the recording of the "Long Road Out of Eden" album with our former producer Bill Szymczyk at the helm. I saw his function as more of a mediator, a consigliere, a ringmaster, if you will. Glenn and I, by that time, had learned how to produce records. In fact, everybody in the band knew what to do, and once we got into the process, it turned out that we didn't really need an overseer. We worked in rotating teams in two

different studios, mine and Glenn's. That enabled us to work on more than one song at a time, and it expedited the process."

7. D- The lyrics police. Timothy explained, "I can tell you a little story. One time, before we recorded 'Hell Freezes Over,' I went over to see Don and Glenn, and we had the basic idea for a song, 'People Can Change'. I had a whole legal pad full of ideas, and you know how your second-grade teacher used to take a red pen to mark your work and cross things off? That's what Don did! I didn't take offense to it. He's good at what he does."

8. A- The lone arranger. It was a tribute to his crucial part in writing the band's classic songs. Henley recalled, "We all get too close to things to see them sometimes, and it's great to have him come in. If I get stuck, he's great at unsticking. He wrote some of the best parts of "Hotel California" and "Desperado," too. I get credit for a lot of that, but the fact is that he wrote some of the pivotal lines that I wouldn't have thought of in a million years. He's great at arranging, too — his nickname is The Lone Arranger.

9. False. Don was enraged by the use of his music in what he views as an unethical way. Don says, "You can't rewrite the lyrics to somebody else's songs, record it, and put it on the internet." He later added, "Some of these young kids have grown up in a world that doesn't understand or respect copyright material or intellectual property. They look at songs as interactive playthings." Henley is also not a fan of Ocean, more generally. "I didn't think he was cool. I thought he was a talentless little prick. And I still do."

10. False. The band values a good hit single and produces them intentionally. Henley says, "Hit singles are no crime. But, unfortunately, some people view them to be something that can't be good artistically, and that's total nonsense as far as I'm concerned. The way the record business is structured these days ... if you don't have singles, you can forget it. You can work for ten years making eclectic and artistic underground albums, and maybe you'll get the recognition you deserve when you're half-dead."

11. C- Ringo Starr. Joe is married to Marjorie Bach, who

is the sister of Barbara, Ringo's wife. Joe and Ringo have been very close friends for several decades and have often recorded together. He says, "Well, we are involved with each other's projects. I've played on his last couple of albums, and we've known each other since the '80s. It turned into a family business. He played on my album, so I had to play on his album. Then I played on his album, so he had to play on mine. We really enjoy working together. We always have, but now it's special because he's my brother-in-law."

12. False. But she did say a member of the Eagles was the love of her life. Stevie had a relationship with Joe Walsh in the mid-1980s and has referred to Joe as the "great, great love of my life." Walsh also remembers her fondly and says, "We spent about a year together, and she helped me write a bunch of music, and I helped her write her music. We had a great relationship. Romantically, it shifted, but in terms of friends and respect for each other, that's all still there. She's really a great person. Anybody who knows her will tell you that. And she's a national treasure.

Anything she sings, you immediately know it's her. If it's on the radio, you don't change stations; you listen to it."

13. False. He still has a soft spot for the classic song. When asked about being sick of the song, Walsh replied, "I should be, but I'm not. That song is really hard to play the right way. Some of the other songs are automatic, and it's not as exciting to play them as it used to be. But with "Hotel California," I really have to sit up straight and pay attention to play it right. So that's one of the songs I look forward to because that it's still a challenge."

14. False. The band knows that they are considered a nostalgia act and are at peace with that. Don says many fans listen to the new stuff "to recapture their lost youth. There's an association with our music with some of the best times in their lives. We wrote the soundtrack to a lot of people's lives — as did many other groups. We're not the only ones. So, I think that's a great part of it, although I'm told that many high school kids are discovering us now. That's good."

15. True. In 2016, he said there was no way the band could continue without its leader. As he put it, "I don't see how we could go out and play without the guy who started the band." He even added, "It would just seem like greed or something," says Henley. "It would seem like a desperate thing." However, a few months later, there were already signs that Don was changing his mind. He said, "You know, Glenn has a son who can sing and play quite well. And one of the only things that would make sense to me is if it were his son." He added, "There have been no discussions along those lines, and we're still going through the healing process — trying to get through all of this, but those are things that might happen somewhere down the road."

16. A- *Fast Times at Ridgemont High*. Crowe was deeply connected to the Eagles, and his movie, *Almost Famous*, about a fictional band, was partially inspired by his time covering the band. Meanwhile, the Russell Hammond character was inspired by Glenn Frey. Cameron remembers, "It was easy to share your personal stuff with Glenn. He'd help you plot

out the answers to your problems like a seasoned coach. He once laid out the psychology of getting and maintaining a buzz at a party. Two beers back-to-back, then one every hour and 15 minutes ... You'll be loquacious, and all the girls will talk with you." Cameron hired Glenn to play in his movie *Jerry Maguire*. He wanted to hire him again for a 2016 TV show called "Roadies." Crowe said, "I was set on hiring Glenn to play the band's skilled but flighty manager, Preston. The word that came back was upsetting. Frey was in tough shape, hospitalized but fighting. I tried not to worry too much. Glenn Frey is, and always was, built for the fourth-quarter win."

17. Trick question. They didn't snub anyone. Unlike many other bands, the guys did the right thing and acknowledged everyone who contributed to their incredible legacy. At the time, Glenn said, "You try to be a bit blasé about it, but when it actually hits you, it's pretty nice ... I'm especially happy all seven Eagles have been recognized because everybody contributed."

18. True. Or technically not wholly accurate. Felder sued

Glenn and another anonymous individual (probably Don Henley) for wrongful termination. He complained that Henley and Frey "insisted that they each receive a higher percentage of the band's profits." And that he was terminated for insisting on getting a fair share. The case was settled out of court for an undisclosed sum.

19. B- Bernie Leadon. Meisner was invited but refused the offer. Felder was not invited due to the legal beef with the band. Joe was very excited and said, "Bernie's brilliant, I never really got a chance to play with him, but we've been in contact. We see him from time to time, and I'm really glad he's coming because it's going to take the show up a notch, and I'm really looking forward to playing with him, finally."

20. C- His son. Deacon was born in 1993 and, at age 24, replaced his deceased father in one of the most famous bands in the world. Don explained somewhat poetically, "There's an old system both in Eastern and Western culture called the guild system where the father is the master and the son is the

apprentice. The trade, the craft, the business is handed down from father to son. I think it's the only appropriate way to carry on. I don't think I'd do it otherwise. Since it's Glenn's blood, it's his son; I think that's appropriate."

DID YOU KNOW?

- Don and Glenn were very unhappy with Don Felder's tell-all book, *Heaven and Hell: My Life in the Eagles*. But, Henley says, "The fact is, we are largely responsible both for the longevity and the success of this band. Because we did it our way, and a lot of people didn't like that. Felder's just bitter because he got kicked out of the group, so he decided to write a nasty little tell-all, which I think is a really low, cheap shot. I mean, I could write some stuff about him that would make your mustache curl."

- The Eagles were fortunate in surviving the debauchery of the 1970s. Don remembers, "Everybody was doing it. It was the '70s; it was what everybody was doing, which doesn't make it right necessarily. And you know, looking back on it, there are some regrets about that. We probably could have been more productive … although we were pretty productive, considering." But Joe thinks that the drugs and liquor also helped with creativity. The guitarist says, "Could Hendrix have played like that sober, straight, and without acid? I don't think so. Could Hemingway and Faulkner have written like that unless they were alcoholics? Probably not. I always used that as a crutch in my denial — that artists should experience all extremes. But it never occurred to me that all those people are dead. Being a rock 'n roller and partying was part of the times back then. I took it as far as I could go, and it almost killed me."

- Joe Walsh had a tough time getting sober. He had lived in a haze of drugs and alcohol for so long that he didn't know what to do after quitting. Joe remembers, "I've been sober for 18 years now. It wasn't like you flick a switch, and you're sober. It takes a while. You have to learn how to do everything all over again. You can measure how long that takes in terms of years. What I didn't know at the time was how to write music and do rock 'n roll and live rock 'n roll and record sober. I didn't try to do that at first. I learned how to take care of myself and then play in front of people. I didn't tackle going back to rock 'n roll until I had some sobriety under my belt."

- Whereas most bands that lived in the fast lane lost members, they mostly came out of their hectic days healthy and sane. When asked why, Don explained, "We were binge-purge people. We didn't debauch all the time. We had our periods of cleaning up. Plus, we're genetically lucky, working-class kids from blue-collar backgrounds. We're a bunch of tough little sons of bitches." Like many of the veteran bands still around, the Eagles live a different lifestyle nowadays. Don says nowadays, "Our concerts are so sedate; there's no partying, no alcohol, it's like a morgue backstage."

- Glenn repaired his relations with Bernie Leadon towards the end of his life. Bernie apologized for pouring the beer on Glenn in that final fight. When he rejoined the band for the "History of the Eagles" tour, the two rediscovered their friendship. Leadon recalls, "He gave me a big, huge thanks for participating. Then he said, 'It's been really awesome to have you back out there. This is not the end.'" Unfortunately, it was.

- One of the secrets to the band's ability to navigate the music business relatively unscathed was the management of Irving Azoff. Often touted as the most powerful man in the music business, Azoff has been working with the Eagles for decades. Known as a very tough and intimidating individual, Henley once said of him, "He's Satan, but he's our Satan." However, today the singer says of Irving, "He's mellowed. He used to be a holy terror. Some of that reputation is undeserved. He'll go to the mat for his artists. But if you're the enemy — look out."

- The key partnership between Don Henley and Glenn Frey was the heart of the band's success. It continued all the way through to their last album as a band, 2007's "Long Run Out of Eden." After recording that album, Don said, "We had both become more adept at the process of songwriting, more comfortable and confident as writers. Melody and lyrics were just as important — maybe more so — than ever. But there wasn't as much flailing around, trying to find a direction, not as much doubt. Again, we had the luxury of time; we did a lot of touring during the making of that album." Of course, many other musicians played an essential role in the band, but they were the engine together. For that reason, Don says that Glenn's death is the end of the band. "It doesn't seem feasible to me. Glenn was such a pivotal part; I mean, he was the leader of the band, and it would be pretty strange going forward without him." Many observers saw and appreciated Frey's outsized role in the band. Linda Ronstadt's manager John Boylan said, "Glenn was the driving force. Ambitious and talented as hell and just driven. Henley, an intellectual, thinker, tremendous singer, and really good drummer. Randy was a solid bass player and a great high harmony singer, and a great lead singer, too. Bernie's just a mensch, man. One of the great people in our business." Like all great bands, they were greater than the sum of their parts.

It remains to be seen what the future holds for the Eagles. With the death of Glenn Frey, they lost their leader and half of the driving force that has driven their remarkable success. But whatever the future holds, the canon of songs and albums the Eagles have produced cement their eternal place in the American songbook.

We hope you have enjoyed this delve into the life and times of America's most successful band. So, excuse us while we step away from these challenging questions and relax to "Tequila Sunrise."

Printed in the USA
CPSIA information can be obtained
at www.ICGtesting.com
CBHW051651281024
16400CB00062B/930